Giles's
London

This collection first published in 2007 by
Express Newspapers
The Northern & Shell Building
10 Lower Thames Street
London EC3R 6EN

ISBN-13: 978-08507-9342-0

Cover design and typesetting by Production Relief, London, UK

London

Edited by John Field

Express Newspapers™

Dedicated to my grandchildren –
Edward, Florence, Millie, Hebe, Cicely and Monty –
with the wish that they have lots of laughter throughout their lives.

"Mum! Grandma's gone down behind the piano."

Daily Express, December 28th, 1974

Acknowledgement – I would like to acknowledge the various books about Carl Giles and his work, written by Peter Tory, who had the luck to interview Giles, on a number of occasions, about his life. I have gleaned most of my information about Giles's links with London from these books.

Introduction

Although Carl Giles lived for most of his life near Ipswich in Suffolk, he never really severed his strong connections with London, where he was born. The capital remained a major source of inspiration for his work throughout his life, and many of its buildings and scenes appear in his cartoons. This book contains a collection of these London cartoons, which illustrate both his artistic skills and his deep affection for the city.

When Giles left London to live in Suffolk at the age of twenty-seven, Lionel Lambourne, former Head of Paintings at the Victoria and Albert Museum, said that the cartoonist was going back to his spiritual home, as the Giles family came from that county. That, probably, was true, but there is no doubt that for the rest of his life, London remained his spiritual 'home-from-home'.

Giles at home in Suffolk

After the Second World War, Giles quickly settled down happily at Hillbrow Farm, a few miles outside Ipswich, and became a farmer as well as a cartoonist. This move was an enormous change in lifestyle compared with his earlier life in London, but he adapted quickly to the changes. In looking at his work, it is obvious that the significant differences between these two halves of his life – one half part of a great world city and the other entrenched in a very rural part of East Anglia – delighted and entertained him, and strongly influenced his cartoons. This sharp contrast in lifestyles added an important dimension to the breadth of subjects covered in Giles's drawings and was often at the heart of their humour.

An important factor that influenced much of his work was that he maintained strong links with the city of his birth and made, almost to the end, regular and frequent visits to it. In this way he was able to replenish continuously his connections with London, and his love and feel for the city and its people shone through all the London cartoons produced throughout his career. This book celebrates and records the drawings that resulted from that life-long relationship.

Giles the Londoner

While his family came from Newmarket in Suffolk (his grandfather was a jockey who rode for King Edward VII), Giles was born in London. He was born on 29 September 1916, next to a pub close to the Angel in Islington. He was christened Ronald, but acquired the nickname Carl based on a supposed resemblance, as a boy, to Boris Karloff.

This start was to be the first contact with London in a life that contained a continuous thread of links with many parts of the city and its world. These links included growing up there, his school days, starting work as an office boy in the city, the Blitz, being involved with the capital's business and entertainment worlds, knowing and understanding the typical Londoner and his humour, contacts with royalty and politicians, and much more. It can also be said that this London start began a long and happy association with the world of the traditional British pub.

During the first part of his life, Giles lived and worked in a number of different areas of London and this, no doubt, helped to give him his deep knowledge of the city and its buildings, as well as develop his obvious affection for the place.

Giles's early years were spent in Islington, but when he was ten the family moved to Edgware. He left school at the age of fourteen to become an office boy for an advertising agency, Superads, on Charing Cross Road. He soon was promoted to the animation studio as an 'in-betweener', creating film cartoon movement, a position that provided the young Giles with rigorous graphic training. It was said that between the ages of sixteen and eighteen, Giles became 'one of the best in-betweeners in the business'.

In 1935, at the age of eighteen, he moved to work at Elstree, in the studio of the film-maker Alexander Korda, where he became an animator for a full-length cartoon feature film called *The Fox Hunt*. During Giles's time there, Korda moved his office to Isleworth and Giles went with it. Unfortunately, the film was not a commercial success and Giles then accepted a job, still in animation, with Roland Davies. Davies's studio was based in Museum Street, Ipswich, and this job took Giles away from London for the first time. There he worked on six black-and-white films, during 1936 and 1937, featuring the then well-known cartoon character, 'Steve the Horse'.

Just before the beginning of the war Giles returned to London, where he got his first full-time job as a cartoonist with Reynolds News, the Sunday paper whose offices were situated at the top end of Gray's Inn Road, near King's Cross. During this period, he continued to develop his cartooning skills and also got to know, intimately, the various pubs in the Fleet Street area used by the journalists, such as the King's Head and the Pindar of Wakefield.

Giles remained in London throughout the wartime Blitz. Both he and Joan, the girl who would become his wife, lived and worked in a very dangerous part of London. Joan's house and Giles's office were both located on a lethal line that linked the primary railway targets of Liverpool Street, Euston, King's Cross and St. Pancras, Marylebone, and Paddington stations. In April 1941, Joan, now Giles's fiancée, was at home with her parents in Great Percy Street, when a stick of bombs straddled the house, causing great damage. Joan escaped, relatively unharmed, but other people living in the same street were killed. During the raid, Giles had remained working at his office not far away. When he realised that Joan's house was in an area where a number of bombs had dropped that night, he rushed over there and, finding it destroyed, feared that she and her family were dead. It was not until the next morning that he found out they had all survived. Following the destruction of their home, Joan and her family moved to a flat in Finchley, while Giles continued living with his parents in Edgware.

On 14 March 1942, Giles married Joan at St. John's Church in East Finchley, and they spent their honeymoon night in the Dickens's Suite of the Great White Horse Hotel in the centre of Ipswich. They began married life in a rented cottage in the village of Tuddenham, on the outskirts of the town.

In September 1943, after a great deal of enticement by John Gordon, the then editor of the Sunday Express, Giles moved from Reynold's News to the Express Group, and his first cartoon appeared for them in the Sunday Express in October of that year. Giles became a war correspondent for the Group, with the rank of Captain, and on 19 September 1944 began his journey to the front in Belgium as a cartooning war correspondent. With his war cartoons – displaying the life of the troops in the field and depicting 'tommies, G.I.s and jerries' – Giles built up a strong reputation across the country and was well known nationally by the time he returned to the UK.

After the war ended, Giles and Joan decided to make Suffolk their home and, in October 1946, they moved to Hillbrow Farm near Witnesham, some four miles outside Ipswich, where they remained for the rest of their lives.

Giles never really wanted to work in the City after settling in Suffolk. John Gordon once stated that Giles 'loathes town and prefers the quieter sociability of Ipswich' and apparently Lord Beaverbrook, Chairman of the Express Group, frequently complained that it was almost impossible to get Giles up to London for office meetings.

Despite these comments, however, he did make regular visits to the city. Every ten days or so he would visit the capital, not to deliver his work – which was sent by train and taxi – but with the purpose of having a good time in selected drinking establishments with friends. In those days, there were a number of pubs well-used by the newspaper men of Fleet Street, including the Albion on Ludgate Circus on the corner of Fleet Street, the Punch, towards the Strand, and the Eight Bells, opposite the black façade of the Daily Express building. It is said that Giles's two favourites were the 'Poppins' (actually called the Red Lion), tucked into the side of the Daily Express building, and the famous El Vino but, doubtless, Giles also knew the others quite well.

He never, therefore, allowed his connections with London to weaken, and, in fact, retained strong links throughout the years. With the exception of the period at Roland Davies's studio in Ipswich he was, for the whole of his career, employed by city-based companies, primarily, of course, the Express Group. This, and his regular jaunts to London, ensured that his links with the capital never diminished.

Giles the Artist

It has been said that Giles never had an art lesson in his life; his only formal training was attending anatomy classes at night school. Despite this, his work received much acclaim, not only for its humour, but also for the quality of the artwork. Lionel Lambourne said of him, 'His work takes its place in the great tradition of English humorous draughtsmanship which goes back to Rowlandson and Hogarth'. Lambourne also considered that Giles had a 'genius for social observation combined with serious draughtsmanship'.

Charles Dierick, Artistic Director of the Belgian Centre for Cartoon Art, said in the programme for the exhibition of Giles's work in Brussels (held in, 1994 to commemorate the 50th anniversary of the liberation of Belgium) that 'Truly, Giles is a major artist of our time', and added that the exhibition 'does not intend to prove how great an artist Giles is. Giles's work is going to do that in its own way and the demonstration will be more forceful than anything else. Just come and look'.

There is no doubt that Giles had natural talent as an artist. His drawings, architecturally, are very skilled, and illustrate a strong awareness of things such as perspective, balance of dark and light, and solid and void. It is obvious that he took great pleasure from drawing on a blank sheet of paper or board and capturing the character and beauty of a façade, or the glimpse of a corner, or the way an imposing building influenced or changed a particular view. Many of the cartoons chosen for this book clearly illustrate his artistic appreciation of architecture and townscape.

Giles's cartoons were usually very accurate in terms of architectural detail. Lionel Lambourne stated that he was 'blessed with a phenomenal visual memory', and added that he had 'an amazing eye for detail'. On occasions, however, Giles would introduce an element of artistic licence and some cartoons display such anomalies as a composite street scene, with two parts of the same street appearing, in the one drawing, in an incorrect juxtaposition to one another. Perhaps he did it for the sake of amusement and to confuse his audience or, maybe, he simply preferred the final artistic composition. Some examples of these 'inaccuracies' have been included in this book and are referred to in the individual cartoon texts.

He used a variety of drawing media – ink and watercolour, pencil/crayon, washes and tints; his illustrations ranged from precise drawings of a building and its architecture, to more sketchy impressions, which, nevertheless, captured the essential elements of the scene, making it instantly recognisable. He was also a master at capturing a scene from a variety of viewpoints, from the worm's-eye view through to the bird's-eye view, as well as from human eye-level. Sometimes, the whole building or its façade was shown but occasionally it was just a detail such as a corner or a doorway.

Giles's cartoons display the pure joy he obviously felt in sketching and drawing. Often, the drawings went beyond the needs of the cartoon – the point of the humour illustrated would have been equally achieved without such a detailed background. He did not need to draw the architectural features of a building in such depth, or the accuracy of a uniform, or the many other small details that he placed in his drawings. We can conclude, therefore, that he introduced this level of detail purely for the sake of art and for the sheer pleasure of drawing.

There are some cartoons where the setting of the humour does, in fact, add greatly to the point being made. An imposing building can be an extremely effective setting if the comedy revolves around puncturing the pomposity of some grandee, or a setting where a more ordinary person is not daunted at all by the grandeur of his or her surroundings. Giles frequently used the setting of the cartoon, in this way, to great effect.

Over the years, Giles often illustrated the same building in a number of different cartoons; consequently, the collection selected for this book includes more than one drawing of the same building, though each is drawn from a different viewpoint or in a different style. In these cases, it is interesting to compare his artistic treatment of the same building or scene.

A further point to be noted is that each time he did a drawing, it was unique to that specific cartoon. On occasion, he simply could have copied or modified an earlier drawing of a particular location and adapted it to suit the point of humour being made. Giles did not do this. He went to the trouble of preparing a completely new sketch for each cartoon. Perhaps he liked the challenge of drawing the building from a different position, or he felt that the new viewpoint or drawing style better met the demands of the humour, or perhaps, again he did it simply for the pleasure of drawing.

The success of his cartoons, of course, relied upon the lively mixture of humour, social awareness, and art they contained. Many cartoonists do not feel the need to give their characters a recognisable setting. Giles was one of the few who developed this as an art form and this approach gave an outstanding quality to his work.

Over his almost fifty years of creating cartoons, Giles studied and captured on paper many of London's most important and historic buildings. Approximately fifty of the city's buildings and places are covered by the cartoons in this book. They include such a wide range of London's built heritage that it has been necessary to divide them into groups of similar building uses to give some order to this large collection. The cartoons included here illustrate Giles's obvious affection for the capital city and its wealth of grand and imposing buildings and spaces. As a body of work, his cartoons form a unique and attractive artistic record of many of the best-loved buildings in our capital city.

Giles and London Characters

It is obvious from his cartoons that Giles was delighted and amused by the people who made up the everyday London scene. His drawings captured the broad mix of people who form a typical crowd on the streets of London. They ranged from the rather grand, and sometimes pompous, city and ceremonial types to the ordinary 'man in the street'; from the bewildered tourists to the cheeky cockney; from the self-important symbols of authority to the usually uncontrollable Giles family. Therefore, a chapter of this book has been devoted to cartoons that illustrate Giles's fascination with the characters who inhabit our capital and whom he was able to capture so well in his drawings.

Peter Tory, his colleague at the Express Group, felt that 'Giles was entertained by the anarchy of his world'. He made gentle fun of people but was hardly ever cruel. His drawings successfully captured our nation's life and culture, with its qualities of humour, grumbling, superiority, stoicism, cynicism, uncertainty, arrogance, straightforwardness, pomposity, and many more – all features that we have to accept are part of our society. Giles had the skill to accurately portray all of these characteristics – good and bad – in his drawings.

His work covered an unsettling and changing period of our history – loss of power and our shrinking role in world affairs, memories of war, nationalisation, and surviving in an increasingly competitive world. The ability to illustrate – with humour, understanding, and even affection – all this, along with the more mundane aspects of our daily lives, is what made him so loved as a cartoonist.

Giles's cartoons speak to, and are enjoyed by, all levels of our society. Equally, the characters inhabiting his cartoon world encompass the broad range of people and groups who make up our society, from the man in the street to the monarch.

Giles saw comedy in many aspects of our national life and this would often form the basis of his cartoons' humour. This included things such as ordinary characters who are totally unfazed by the overwhelming grandness of their surroundings, for example the cleaner, going about her daily work in the Houses of Parliament, surrounded by the 'pomp and circumstance' of one of our great institutions, but concerned only about her box of Persil, or the little man, in his Carnaby Street mock-military outfit, completely undaunted by the fact that he is being severely chastised by a disdainfully superior Guards Officer, in the middle of Horse Guards Parade. The concept of two of our elected Members of Parliament pausing at a burger van for some sustenance, after a very late night sitting in the House, and surrounded by members of London's rather obscure early-morning life obviously also appealed.

Giles was always on the side of the ordinary man, fighting and often losing against an unthinking higher authority: the little man in the dock about to be sentenced to death for contravening the parking laws twice in one year, with the smugly satisfied traffic warden on the witness stand; or the ex-soldier at Buckingham Palace wishing to return his war medals to the Queen in protest against the Poll Tax, but finding himself being sent back home by an appalled guardsman to clean them properly.

Another delightful element of his humour was that his cartoon world was one that frequently involved a collision of characters from completely different walks of life and that was, often, the essence of the charm, allure and humour of his cartoons. Examples include the group of London 'spivs' – as they were then called – contemplating the chances of selling to a stampede of 'horsey' folk from the shire some rather dodgy tickets for Liberace or the ballet; the old farmhand, undoubtedly from Suffolk, giving his rustic views on how to deal with London's traffic problems; and a passing city gent and the 'seen-it-all-before' policeman addressing a motley crew of weekend sailors about their unfashionable attire.

Giles was enthralled by the dynamics and vigour of London life and, with his gift for social observation, was able to capture all this energy through the various characters he drew.

Giles the National Figure

Although Carl Giles came from a fairly ordinary background, his work became so highly regarded that it took him to the highest circles in society. Royalty, politicians, and entertainers all knew of him and most, if not all of them, greatly admired and enjoyed his work and this led him to friendships, some quite close, with many well-known figures. At the same time, he was totally content when enjoying a drink with a group of friends back home in Suffolk in one of the many pubs he considered his local.

Giles, as President of the British Cartoonists' Association, with Princess Margret in 1970

He was quite happy to include anyone within his cartoon world, including his one-time boss Lord Beaverbrook, and the Royal Sovereign and her family, as well as characters whom he met regularly in one of his local pubs. He also included authoritarian figures, such as a particular Ipswich traffic warden whom he had run up against on several occasions. Despite the high regard Lord Beaverbrook had for Giles and his work, they rarely met socially. When Beaverbrook's son Max Aitkin took over the business, though, on his father's death in 1964, there was a strong contrast in their relationship. Aitkin had an obvious admiration for Giles and his sense of humour and, also, his ability to enjoy life to the full. Aitkin and Giles – 'tycoon's son and former cockney scallywag', as described by Peter Tory in his book *A Life in Cartoons* – became close socially. Sharing a strong interest in sailing, Giles would stay at the Aitkin's house in Cowes and, in London, Aitkin and Giles would lunch together regularly at the Hyde Park Hotel.

In 1959, Giles was awarded an OBE for his contribution to the cartoon world, and, during the sixties, he found himself gradually being adopted as a kind of cartooning court jester to the royal family. He began a habit of sending sketches to the Palace, to mark various incidents and royal events, and would receive delighted letters in return. The highpoint, probably, in this respect, was in the summer of 1962, when the Queen invited Giles to lunch with her at the Palace.

It was not unusual for the Queen to ask for the original of a cartoon that had particularly amused her – mainly cartoons containing a royal reference. An example is the cartoon with the Queen in a demonstration outside a bookie's office along with Lord Rosebury, the celebrated racehorse owner, which, obviously, entertained her greatly, and the original is said to now hang in the Queen's apartments. Peter Tory, again in his book, *A Life in Cartoons*, records that the royals, between them, have thirty-six of Giles's originals, with Prince Phillip alone having fifteen.

It is interesting to note that, when Prince Charles and Princess Anne gave a dinner in honour of their parents' silver wedding anniversary in November 1972, they asked Giles to provide the cover illustration for the dinner programme. As shown, he chose perhaps his best-loved character, Grandma, as the basis for the humour it contained.

Included in his wide circle of friends and admirers were a number of well-known members of the entertainment world. Before his sixtieth birthday party, held at Hillbrow Farm, an impromptu pre-party drinking session took place in the Barley Mow in Witnesham, a pub that appears in at least two of his locally based cartoons. The locals were more than a little surprised when stage and television personalities Tommy Cooper, Eric Sykes, Warren Mitchell, and Johnny Speight (who wrote the extremely successful *Til death us do part* television series in which Mitchell played the wonderful Alf Garnett) arrived at the pub with Giles, on their way to the farm, for a longish pre-party drink. Not surprisingly, it is said that the humour and laughter was non-stop until the group finally left, belatedly, for the party itself.

"Six silver spoons for Her Majesty and his Royal Highness from a lady with the initials B.R."

The wide range of important personalities, mainly from the entertainment world, who were happy to provide the forewords for his cartoon Annuals, illustrates his fame throughout the country. From further afield, Frank Sinatra wrote in his foreword to the thirty-third Annual (1977–78): 'To Carl – who has been so kind to me through the years and who, I believe, to be one of the funniest men in the world – Affectionately, Francis Albert'.

In 1962, Giles received from the Cartoonists' Club of Great Britain a Special Award for 'Distinguished Services to Cartooning' and in the 1970s he was made President of the British Cartoonist's Association. In 1984, he was made Life-President of the Royal National Lifeboat Institute, for which he had drawn and donated Christmas cards for many years. In 1990, he was awarded Senior Fellowship of the Royal College of Art. In April 2000, five years after his death, he was voted 'Britain's favourite cartoonist of the twentieth century' and, in 2005, the Press Gazette chose him as one of the forty journalists in its Newspapers Hall of Fame.

Carl Giles became a nationally known and well-loved figure, admired not only throughout this country, but also in many parts of the English-speaking world. He always retained his warmth for the ordinary man and was always happiest when with his friends, either in a bar in the capital, in a pub in one of his local villages, or in nearby Ipswich. He may have rubbed shoulders regularly with the great and the good, but there is no doubt that his feet were firmly planted alongside those of the ordinary people of Britain.

Giles's Legacy

Carl Giles died on 7 August 1995, seven months after his wife Joan. It is fitting, perhaps, that he is buried with Joan in the small village churchyard at Tuddenham, two miles from his farm and one hundred yards or so from the village pub, The Fountain, which features in a number of his cartoons and where he spent many pleasant evenings surrounded by friends. The grave is quite simple – just their names and dates – and there is no reference to his career or the importance of his contribution to the nation's sense of self-awareness. There is nothing carved on the gravestone, apart from his name and reference to his OBE, to indicate that the final resting place of a man known to most people in this country and many outside it, is in this quiet country churchyard.

There are, however, some important reminders around. There is a recent small housing development in Witnesham, the village nearest his farm, called Giles Way. A statue by Miles Robinson of some of the members of his cartoon family, including Grandma and Vera, has been placed outside his old office in the centre of Ipswich, with Grandma looking up to the window of the room where Giles spent many years producing his cartoons. While he was still alive, Giles officially opened a pub named in his honour – The Giles – that is located close to the area in London where he was born.

His main legacy, however, must be the great wealth of his artwork, comprising over seven thousand cartoons, and the enormous amount of laughter and humour it brought to the people of Britain, and elsewhere, for almost half a century.

J.F.

Palaces and Castles

Palaces and Castles

Buckingham Palace was originally a town house that was owned, from the beginning of the eighteenth century, by the Dukes of Buckingham. George III purchased it in 1761 to be a comfortable family home close to St. James's Palace. In 1762, it was remodelled by Sir William Chambers to meet the king's needs. During the late 1820s, under George IV, John Nash transformed the house into a palace. It has served as the official London residence of Britain's sovereign since 1837, when Queen Victoria took up residence. The East Wing, which fronts the Mall, was completed in 1847 to a design by the architect Blore, and this required the removal of the Marble Arch, which now stands in Hyde Park. This façade was refaced and redesigned in 1913 by Sir Aston Webb. The palace has 775 rooms.

St. James's Palace is the senior Palace of the Sovereign with a long history as a royal residence. Built by Henry VIII, much survives from his building, including the Chapel Royal, the gatehouse, some turrets and two surviving Tudor rooms in the State apartment. Constructed between 1531–36, it was the residence of kings and queens of England for over three hundred years. Today it is the London home of several members of the royal family and their household offices, and is often used for official functions.

William III bought **Kensington Palace** in 1689 and commissioned Sir Christopher Wren to extend and improve the house, which included the construction of royal apartments for the king and queen, a Council Chamber, the Chapel Royal, and the Great Stairs. It was the working royal residence of successive sovereigns until 1760 and was the birthplace and childhood home of Queen Victoria. Today, the palace accommodates the offices and London residences of several members of the royal family.

Clarence House was built between 1825–27 to a design by John Nash for Prince William Henry, Duke of Clarence, who became King William IV. During its history the house has been altered to reflect the changes in occupancy over nearly two centuries. It was the London home of Queen Elizabeth, the Queen Mother (from 1953 until her death in 2002), and is now the official London residence of the Prince of Wales and the Duchess of Cornwall.

The **Tower of London** – the earliest structure was built by William the Conqueror, with the foundations of The White Tower being laid in 1078. With many improvements and additions over the centuries, The White Tower developed into the wonderful complex of fortress, palace, castle and museum we see today. The Crown Jewels, containing many irreplaceable and historic pieces, are on display in the Jewel House at the Tower. In the past, the Tower also served as a prison and a place of execution and was the scene of many historical events.

Windsor Castle, high above the River Thames and on the edge of a Saxon hunting ground, is an official residence of the Queen and the oldest and largest occupied castle in the world. William the Conqueror chose the site in the 1070s, and over the years it has been inhabited continuously, and altered and refurbished by successive monarchs. A royal home and fortress for over nine hundred years, the castle remains a working palace today.

'You and your "Let's call at the Palace and invite him to you New Year party while his Mum and Dad are away".'

Prince Charles was just over five years old at this time. His parents were in New Zealand as part of a
royal tour of Commonwealth countries following the Queen's Coronation in June 1953.

'Good morning, Madam, aren't we the lady that got done for sending Her Majesty six British Railway spoons for her Silver Wedding?'

This refers to one of Grandma's many earlier misdemeanours (see drawing in the introduction.).

Note that the same policeman is involved. This occasion is the Queen's fiftieth birthday.

'We must teach Your Royal Highness that it is imprudent to fill in forms: "My Mum doesn't work".'

This is an unusual view of the front façade of the Palace. When he was fourteen, Prince Andrew went on a school exchange holiday in Toulouse, France.
He stated, as part of an elaborate ploy to keep his identity secret, that his father was a gentleman farmer, his mother did not work, and that his name was Edward.
The family he stayed with was in on the secret.

ON THE TRAIL OF THE STURGEON

'Thank you, no – we've had fish once this week.'
(This week a sturgeon was presented to Buckingham Palace.)

In compliance with a tradition dating back to Edward II (1284–1327), a Grimsby fish merchant offered to send a large sturgeon (40 lbs) to the Queen.
The acceptance telegram from the Queen arrived late, by which time the fish had been sold to another fish merchant in Somerset.
An urgent drive through a foggy early morning to London got the fish back to the Palace.

'A white puff means Enoch Powell is talking through his hat, a black puff means their oil heater needs a new burner'

This refers to Enoch Powell, possibly the most controversial politician in British politics since the Second World War – with strong views on many subjects.

'Thank the Press for printing that story about the American following the band at the White House.'

Disappointed that the White House was closed to visitors on the day he was in Washington, an American joined in at the back of a Marine Band and marched into the grounds.
He then proceeded to wander around the White House reception rooms before going upstairs into the President's private quarters and was finally discovered sitting at the Reagan's dining table.
The President's entire security system was asked 'How did this happen?'. Their response was not recorded.

'With the greatest respect for your tattered nerves – PUT IT OUT.'

The Grenadier Guardsman represents the nation awaiting the birth of Prince Andrew, who eventually arrived three days after this cartoon appeared.
Over two thousand people were waiting outside the Palace and a great burst of cheering went up when the bulletin, announcing the birth, was fixed to the Palace railings.

'Anglo–US unity would blossom quicker if the President's bodyguard left their gum outside the Palace.'

President Nixon had lunch with the Queen and members of the royal family at Buckingham Palace during his two-day official visit to London.
He was accompanied by a large group of 'advisers'.

'Playing up 'ell because she couldn't find her woolly egg warmer on show.'

Another rather dubious present from Grandma to members of the Royal Family, this time for the wedding of Prince Charles and Princess Diana.
It has taken four Guardsmen and two beefeaters to control Grandma!

'And that, I presume, is the cot and play pen.'

The Palace, slightly adapted. The newspapers had just announced the forthcoming birth of the first child of Princess Margaret and Anthony Armstrong-Jones.
It was reported that the 'girls in the office' mobbed the father-to-be when he arrived at his office at the Design Centre in Central London that morning.
The children's furniture captures the design trend of the time.

'Whoops! Jack's trod on something sharp.'

Viscount Linley, first child of Princess Margaret and Anthony Armstrong-Jones, now the first Earl of Snowdon, was born on 3 November 1961.
This view of the house is from the Stable Yard Road junction with the Mall.

'Meet the new neighbours, or menu, whichever way you look at it.'

Film star Elizabeth Taylor and her husband Richard Burton hired a large vessel, to be moored near the Tower, in order not to be parted from their four pet dogs.
The dogs had to stay on board because of quarantine restrictions, and were there for two months while the film Where Eagles Fly was made.
One of the dogs was a Pekinese, called Oh Fi, and another was a Yorkshire terrier named E'en So, both of which are featured here.
Note that all ravens appearing in Giles's cartoons have their own little beefeater hats.

'On the fifth step in May 1536, Anne Boleyn paused on her way to the block – and on the sixth step in May 1941,

me and my mates put out a couple of incendiaries.'

(The Tower of London is now reopened to the public.)

The Tower had been closed to the public during the war and used as a military centre and prison for prisoners of war.
Rudolf Hess (Hitler's deputy) was imprisoned there for four days during 1941.

'I only asked her if now that Boots are printing nude holiday snaps she'd mind taking her hat off.'

The Bloody Tower was so named because of its supposed association with the young Princes in the Tower, who disappeared in 1483.
Grandma would choose this spot to have her photograph taken.
Boots the Chemists had just stated that they were now prepared to process holiday snaps showing people in the nude.

'I'm shortly attending a meeting of Fleet Street journalists – these are my measurements...'

A few days earlier, Aneurin Bevan, minister of health, had been forced to announce a Cabinet decision to start charging one shilling per prescription, which he considered to be a blow to the principles of a free health service – presumably the idea of charging was not generally popular, hence Mr Bevan's precautionary steps.

'At the first sound of a Royal Flush we strike up with "All Through the Night" Prestissimo!'

(Prince Phillip announced that Windsor Castle had the noisiest toilets in the kingdom.)

General view of the Round Tower, but Giles decided to show the west end of St. Georges Chapel at the east end of the building – perhaps he preferred the resultant composition.

'Why do I have reason to suspect it is not the Queen? Because the Queen would not use an expression like "Shove off".'

(The Queen had been asked for proof of her identity by a police officer this week.)

Looking up Castle Hill with the Round Tower and Giles's interpretation of Garter House on the left.
The previous weekend the Queen and the Queen Mother had been travelling back to Windsor Castle from a private dinner party when they were stopped by a motorcycle
policeman uncertain about the flashing blue light on the roof of the car. This is not normal procedure for private occasions, thus the policeman's confusion.
Explanations were made and 'within moments' the royal party was on their way.

'As a matter of fact *I* wrote that one about the RSM.'

View up Castle Hill towards St George's Gate. The wall on the right does not exist. Giles, no doubt, needed it in order to include the graffiti.
The 2nd Battalion, Grenadier Guards had asked for police protection from local youths, having been accused of setting fire to their bonfire ten days earliy.

Government

Government

The Houses of Parliament are also known as the Palace of Westminster. The oldest surviving part is Westminster Hall, dating from 1097. Most of the present structure dates from the nineteenth century, when the palace was rebuilt after it was almost entirely destroyed by fire in 1834. Sir Charles Barry and Augustus Welby Pugin were the architects for the building we see today. It is an example of Gothic revival architecture, and most of the work was completed by 1860. The palace contains over one thousand rooms, including the Chambers where the House of Commons and the House of Lords meet to conduct their business.

House of Commons Chamber. Today's chamber opened in 1950, after the original chamber was destroyed by bombs in 1941. Sir Giles Gilbert was the architect for the new chamber, and its design and fittings are more austere than those in the Lords Chamber. It can accommodate only 427 of the 646 Members of Parliament, meaning some Members have to stand during major debates.

House of Lords Chamber. This chamber was completed in 1847 and, with its red benches and ornate gold canopy and throne, is much more lavishly decorated than the Commons Chamber. In front of the throne is the 'Woolsack', a red cushion stuffed with wool, representing the historical importance of the wool trade. The Lord Speaker, who presides over the meetings of the House, uses this. The Sovereign sits on the throne for the State Opening of Parliament and delivers the 'Speech from the Throne', which outlines the Government's legislative agenda for the forthcoming parliamentary session.

10 Downing Street is the residence and office of the prime minister of the United Kingdom. It is at the centre of the British government, both physically and politically. Originally comprising three houses, the building we see fronting Downing Street, with its famous doorway, dates from the 1730s when Robert Walpole, the then prime minister, commissioned the architect William Kent to join the earlier houses together.

The Members of Parliament, of which there are 646, are each chosen by one of the constituencies in the country, through an election. The MPs have three responsibilities: to represent the people of their constituency; to represent their party; and to represent the interests of the country. They are normally members of a political party, without whose disciplines and organisation the House could not properly function. The Speaker, who is an elected member, presides over the Commons Chamber from a canopied seat at one end of the chamber. The Speaker's role is to direct and guide the work of the Commons, to act as Chair during debates, and to see that the rules laid down by the House are correctly observed.

'Poor John – someone's written and blamed him for not feeding our racehorses as well as the French.'

John Strachey, Minister of Food (1946–1950)

There was an outcry because French horses had won, for the first time in history, three of the English racing classics: the Derby (just a few days before the appearance of the cartoon), the Oaks, and the One Thousand Guineas. All sorts of reasons for this national disgrace were put forward.

'I must say, two in the morning of November the Fifth is a strange time to be delivering barrels of frozen herrings to the House of Commons, gentlemen.'

No doubt this refers to the Government's intention, contained in the Queen's Speech at the State Opening of Parliament six days before Guy Fawkes' Night, to reduce the powers of the House of Lords and do away with the hereditary basis on which it was formed.

'MPs' wives – someone let the cat of the bag about the bar being open during these late sessions.'

The day before, 106 MPs had signed a motion that was tabled at the House of Commons proposing that there should be 'no alcoholic liquor of any kind in the House after 10pm'.
The newspaper report suggested that there was very little chance of the motion being debated.

'There you are, Fred – I told you all this celebration's got nothing to do with the opening of the Dairy Show.'

(Parliament and the Dairy Show opened today.)

Both Giles's rural and city lives are encapsulated in this drawing.

'Margaret, I have performed my social obligations and picked you up, but let there be no misapprehensions about you being my mate.'

Outside St Stephen's Entrance at the time of a battle for Tory party leadership and a period of fuel shortages. Edward Heath called a leadership election for 4 February and was widely expected to win but, in fact, Margaret Thatcher won and became the first female leader of a major political party in the UK. At the same time, the government was introducing severe restrictions to combat a major national fuel shortage.

'Great for the old image – "PM saves nation cost of cat".'

This is again outside St. Stephen's Entrance. Edward Heath was prime minister at the time. The House of Commons was suffering an infestation of mice and MPs demanded action.
They requested a squad of cats to combat the growing battalions of mice. This is Giles's solution.

'OK. That's enough of trying to control 'em with iced lollies. Draw batons!'

Campaigning under-fives had gone to No.10 the day before to hand in a petition demanding more nursery schools;
newspapers had a charming photograph of a group clasping their balloons and trying to reach the door-knocker. They also lobbied MPs at the Houses of Parliament.

'Same old mix-up as last year – opening Parliament the same week as the Dairy Show.'

The Churchill Arch leading into the Commons Chamber with, from the left, Ernest Bevin, Aneurin Bevan, Clement Attlee (then prime minister),
Herbert Morrison, Anthony Eden and Winston Churchill, and some of their rural constituents.
There was, in fact, no State Opening of Parliament in 1949, the previous one being 26 October 1948, which did, in fact, coincide with the State Opening of Rarliament.
(se earlier cartoon on page 26.)

"Remind me to have a word with Selwyn after the debate"

Again at the Churchill Arch, Harold Macmillan, then prime minister, comments on his chancellor of the exchequer, John Selwyn-Lloyd.
At this time, Britain's fiscal situation was in a serious situation – at the debate, many MPs were certain that Britain must endure a 'severe and painful economic treatment', and looked to the chancellor to order it.

'You've chained yourself to the wrong railings, Sir – the Prime Minister hasn't lived here since August 1960.'

*Harold Macmillan moved out of No.10 Downing Street to Admiralty House on 3 August 1960, initially for two years,
to allow reconstruction work involving numbers 10, 11 and 12. Obviously the work over-ran.*

'You've chained yourself to the wrong railings, duckie – the Chancellor lives next door.'

It was reported that the chancellor of the exchequer was considering scrapping pensioners' rights to some welfare benefits including the free medical prescriptions and the £10 Christmas bonus. Grandma obviously had an opinion on this.

'So much for Lady Caroline ffrench-Blake cleaning up the Leader's doorstep yesterday.'

Lady Caroline ffrench-Blake and her husband were amongst a group of six people who swept up leaves and cleaned away litter outside No.10 as a 'patriotic gesture' and as a protest about the continuing dustmens' strike.

'OK, knock it off, Marshal Dillon – that's not the purpose of firearm training for the police.'

Following a tragedy eight months prior to this cartoon, in which three London policemen were shot dead, Scotland Yard introduced firearm training for some police. The day prior to the cartoon, the newspaper had run an article about the training for the latest batch of ten policemen undergoing the four-day course.

'Canada's playbout Prime Minister is sure breathing new life into the Commonwealth concept.'

*Prime minister of Canada Pierre Trudeau was attending the Commonwealth Prime Ministers' Conference in London, which opened on 7 January.
Trudeau, a bachelor prime minister, caused a stir by being seen out with a young woman. He said to a journalist:
'You should try a tête-à-tête with someone, with the Mounties and Scotland Yard watching over you'.*

'His boy put it on his head at a Halloween party and he can't get it off.'

The Speaker and some members entering the Commons Chamber from the Members' Lobby, via the Churchill Arch, the day after Hallowe'en.

'I reckon she heard you say "Hear, hear" to Ted's speech at Blackpool.'

The Iron Lady strikes again. It was reported that Margaret Thatcher, the prime minister, was in a stubborn and defiant mood at the end of her party's annual conference, where she had faced major challenges to her authority. 'Ted' Heath was her immediate predecessor as leader of the Conservative Party

'If the Honourable Members over there will kindly stop playing nap, we'll get down to this debate on the corporal punishment of adults.'

The Commons Chamber with the Speaker's chair beneath its canopy. The table of the house, the dispatch boxes and books, and the mace are all accurately shown.
Note the 'sword line', behind which the MPs must remain. The day before, a headmaster had tried to start an International School Children's Union, being an advocate of the rights of children.
For the launch, he booked a hall in London with a capacity of 1,800; it attracted thirteen children – including eight from his own school – and two dozen adults.

'On guard, Bertie – beware the Ides of March.'

Typical members, representing the party in government and Her Majesty's Opposition, as viewed by Giles.
The Labour Party was in power at the time and the prime minister Harold Wilson had survived a crucial vote of confidence the day before, basically ruling out a premature general election.

Monuments and Tourism

Monuments and Tourism

Big Ben is the name generally applied to the Clock Tower, although it really only refers to the main bell inside the tower. The Clock Tower is part of Sir Charles Barry's design for the Houses of Parliament. The clock mechanism was completed in 1854 but the tower itself was not finished until 1858. Augustus Pugin designed the clock faces and dials, which measure seven metres (twenty-one feet) in diameter.

Trafalgar Square commemorates the Battle of Trafalgar (1805). The present square is the design of Sir Charles Barry and was completed in 1845. The architect, Lord Foster, designed a recent upgrading of the area in front of the National Gallery. **Nelson's Column**, built between 1840–43 (almost forty years after Nelson's death), was designed by architect William Railton. Nelson's statue stands 5.5 metres (eighteen feet) tall on top of the column, which is fifty-six metres (185 feet) tall. Sir Edwin Landseer sculpted the four large brass lion made from metal said to come from the cannon of the French Fleet. Sir Edwin Lutyens, architect of the Cenotaph, designed the two large fountains, which were completed in 1939.

The Monument was built between 1671–77 to commemorate the Great Fire of London of 1666. Sir Christopher Wren and Dr. Robert Hooke designed the fluted stone Doric column, which is topped by a gilded urn of fire. Its height – sixty-two metres (202 feet) – marks the distance from its base to the King's baker's shop where the fire started. When it was built, it was the tallest free-standing stone column in the world.

Tower Bridge was built to meet the need to create a link to the increased commercial development in the East End of London. The design, submitted by Horace Jones, the City Architect, was approved in 1884. It took eight years to build and was finally opened by the future King Edward VII in 1894. During its construction, Jones died and his Chief Engineer, Sir John Wolfe-Barry, youngest son of Sir Charles Barry (one of the architects of the Houses of Parliament), and the architect George D. Stevenson took over the project. They replaced Jones's original medieval-style of façade with a more ornate Victorian Gothic style.

Cleopatra's Needle is one of a trio of obelisks now in London, Paris, and New York. Given to the UK in 1819 by Mehemet Ali, viceroy of Egypt, it dates from 1450BC and comes from the Egyptian city of Heliopolis. It was erected on the Victoria Embankment in 1879.

The Embankment extends from the City of Westminster into the City of London and was constructed as part of a scheme to provide London with a modern sewerage system and to provide relief to congestion on the Strand and Fleet Street. Work started in 1865 under the direction of Sir Joseph Bazalgette, the chief engineer, and was completed in 1870. As part of the scheme, two handsome gardens were introduced along the riverfront; one backs onto the government buildings on Whitehall and the other stretches from Hungerford Bridge to Waterloo Bridge.

Marble Arch was designed by the architect John Nash in 1828 and was based upon the Arch of Constantine in Rome. Originally constructed as the entrance to Buckingham Palace, the Arch was found to be too narrow for the grandest coaches and it was moved to its Hyde Park site in 1851.

Whitehall is one of the major routes in central London, running from Parliament Square to Trafalgar Square. Whitehall and the surrounding area is the administrative centre of the United Kingdom, and is dominated by government buildings. It also contains the **Cenotaph**, the country's principal war memorial. Designed by Sir Edwin Lutyens, it was constructed between 1919–20, following the end of the Great War. It carries the words 'The Glorious Dead', chosen by the writer and poet, Rudyard Kipling.

'I sure want to be in the Public Gallery the day he comes out with some of the words I've just taught him.'

The then-minister of education had, at the Conference of the Association of Education Committees, raised the question of the 'traditional exclusive' form of education and stated that 'the best should be made available to all'. Reginald Maudling, then chancellor of the exchequer, expressed concern that the Conservative Party was falling behind and had not been successful in attaining the allegiance of the younger generation because 'they had not yet found a way of talking to them in language they understood'.

'Henry, stop jumping, you'll have the — thing over.'

The day before it had been reported that Big Ben had tilted four inches out of true. A spokesman for the Ministry of Works stated that there was no cause for alarm and added that 'we are watching matters' – presumably from a distance.

"Rare Boys for souvenirs, these Americans."

Giles had a great admiration for the entrepreneurial skills of our American allies.

'Do you still think it was a good idea to bring him up to lobby our MP?'

This relates to the same event that inspired the cartoon, dated two days earlier, included under Houses of Parliament.

'If we had a State Opening of Parliament back home, at least our cops'd let us throw tickertape.'

An illustration of Giles's affection for the informality of our American friends, seen here in contrast to the stiffness of our officers of authority.

'I'll have yer under the unfair trading act!'

The previous day, two men had scaled the sheer sides of Nelson's Column in a four-hour protest climb against British involvement in apartheid in South Africa.
The climb ended with loud applause from the large crowd when the two men reached the top.

'Sit still, Sidney - you'll 'ave the blooming lot over.'

The Victory Day Parade, following the end of WWII, took place in London on 8 June 1946.

' 'Ush! Cyril – it's people like you that make work hard for Mr Graham.'

Billy Graham, the American evangelist, visited London in 1954. Billingsgate Fish Market was formally established by an Act of Parliament in 1699 and remained there until 1982 when it moved to the Docklands. It is understood that, occasionally, colourful language could be heard at the market during the course of its business.

'I don't care if you're trooping the —— colour, get the —— thing ahrt of it.'

The Festival of London started in 1962 to provide a regular summer programme of music and art. In 1968, the Billingsgate Market was still going strong, creating, in Giles's mind at least, the confusion that he loved to capture.

'Well, I'll be glad when this strike's over – I've left my car up there.'

Five weeks into a strike by 9,400 London dockers, in support of 3,800 dockers in Glasgow who were protesting about the proposed redundancy of five hundred of their colleagues. The little man only had to wait a further four days before the dockers in Glasgow voted 1,936 to 340 to return to work. Somehow the Bridge must have been involved.

'Nationalised corned-beef eaters – thats what we are.'

The weekly meat ration had just been reduced to the lowest level endured in this country. At the same time, Parliament decided that the cost of the Beefeaters should be taken off the Civil List,
as His Majestys Privy Purse was experiencing financial difficulties, and should, instead, be covered by the State.
Note the Tower of London in the background.

'Radio the Prime Minister right back and tell him free tickets for Desdemona while we're up here won't appease *us*.'

An armada of sixty-five trawlers, crabbers, and cockleboats sailed up the Thames, into London, in protest about the possible loss of the twelve-mile fishing zone around Britain, to be discussed at the following week's Common Market talks. A stir was being caused at the time by the appearance of a naked young actress playing Desdemona on a West End stage.

"I didn't know the darned thing was loaded"

President Nixon's visit to London coincided with a fairly hectic period. He arrived in Europe just as a major row broke out between France and Britain about a leaked secret discussion between General de Gaulle and Christopher Soames (British ambassador to France) concerning replacing the Common Market with a free trade area. Nixon had, two days before, passed the word to his European allies in Brussels that Russia had hinted its readiness to enter into serious discussions with his administration. The day before suicide squads in Vietnam had thrown themselves at a US artillery base, killing thirty-six marines and wounding 116 others. In Prague, on the same day – the twenty-fifth anniversary of the communist takeover of his country – Jan Zajic protested foreign occupation by turning himself into a human torch; he died from his wounds. Outside Claridge's (Nixon's HQ during his visit), a huge crowd of demonstrators from the National Liberation Front, supporting the North Vietnamese, mounted a noisy and violent protest. It is unlikely that these tumultuous and, in some cases, tragic events were in Giles's mind when he contrived this further unfortunate incident for Nixon.

'In the last scene she gets snake poisoning.'

*Elizabeth Taylor was rushed to hospital from her villa in Rome with an attack of food poisoning.
She and Richard Burton were filming 'Cleopatra', which was released the following year.*

REHEARSAL ON ICE

'But it will be all right on the actual day – there'll be no ice on the roads, so you won't have the Guards slipping base over bayonet every time someone calls " 'Alt!" a bit sharp-like.'

Giles is illustrating the Grenadier Guards doing their best under very hostile conditions.
Although Queen Elizabeth II's Coronation was not to be held until 2 June 1953, this cartoon refers to a rehearsal that took place the previous November on a very cold and frosty morning.

'Latest game – running up and down outside No. 10 and bawling "Windy" through the letter box.'

This is outside the portico of Scotland House on Whitehall, with the Cenotaph in the middle distance. Twenty-one days after this cartoon appeared, the Conservatives lost the general election and Harold Wilson became prime minister.

'I agree with you, mate – the plastic ones are a damn sight lighter.'

A composite drawing – with the sentry box in that position, Giles would then have had to move about two hundred yards up towards Trafalgar Square to get the view of the Old War Department Building as shown on the left of the cartoon. The cartoon relates to tests being undertaken for the Horse Guards to have plastic cuirasses instead of metal, because of the fear of lack of craftsmen in the future who would be capable of hand-making the armour.

'We can't go round thinking everybody riding a horse has escaped from Dartmoor in disguise, Madam.'

The day before it had been discovered that a prisoner described as dangerous had, on occasions, left working parties outside Dartmoor Prison to ride for four miles, on bareback ponies, to a pub.
The farmer who lent him the ponies said that he seemed harmless and, over the months, had got to know him quite well.

Museums, The Arts and Exhibitions

Museums, the Arts and Exhibitions

The British Museum is one of the world's largest and most important museums of human history and culture. It was established in 1753 and was based largely on the collections of Sir Hans Sloane. It was first opened in Montagu House in Bloomsbury, the site of today's museum, in 1759. Sir Robert Smirke designed the neo-classical building we see today. The main building opened in 1847. Smirke's brother Sydney designed The Round Reading Room (1854–57) which was one of the widest domes when built. The Great Hall was roofed in glass and steel to a design by Foster and Partners in 2000.

The Royal Albert Hall of Arts and Sciences is a major venue dedicated to Queen Victoria's husband and consort, Prince Albert. Opened by Queen Victoria in 1871, the Hall has played host to a multitude of different events, and has been affectionately titled 'The Nation's Village Hall'. When first built, it had a capacity of around eight thousand people, but internal changes and modern safety restrictions have reduced it to about 5,545, including standing in the Gallery. The design, by Captain Francis Fowke and Colonel H. Y. Darracott Scott of the Royal Engineers, was influenced heavily by ancient amphitheatres. The Hall has recently undergone a rolling programme of renovation and development (1996–2004) to enable it to meet the demands of the new century's events and performances.

The Royal Opera House serves as the home of the Royal Opera, the Royal Ballet and the Orchestra of the Royal Opera House. There have been two previous theatres on the site. Today's building, with its four-columned portico, dates from 1858, the previous building having been destroyed by fire two years earlier. The architect was Edward Middleton Barry, third son of Sir Charles Barry. It became the Royal Opera House in 1892. It reopened, after the Second World War, in February 1946, with a performance of 'The Sleeping Beauty', having been used as a dance hall during the war years. Major reconstruction work took place between 1996–2000.

Earls Court Exhibition Centre was built as a show centre and dominates the nearby Olympia Exhibition Hall. After some construction delays it finally opened its doors to the public in September 1937. Its capacity is around 19,000 people, including standing room. The Centre is used for exhibitions and as an entertainment venue.

Olympia, originally known as the National Agricultural Hall, was erected in 1886 by Andrew Handyside of Derby. It contains three exhibition halls – known as the Olympia Grand Hall, Olympia National Hall, and Olympia 2 – and is used for a wide variety of major exhibitions.

The Chelsea Flower Show is held annually by the Royal Horticultural Society for five days in May in the grounds of the Royal Hospital Chelsea. The first show was held in 1852 in Kensington and originally was called the Royal Horticultural Society's Great Spring Show. It moved to Chelsea in 1913. Around 157,000 people visit the show each year, the number being restricted by the capacity of the grounds. Two days are open only to members of the RHS, and members of the royal family attend a preview of the show as part of the royal patronage of the Society.

'Pardon me, Tutankhamun, but your tootsies are parked on the double yellow lines.'

The Tutankhamun Exhibition was the most popular exhibition ever held at the British Museum, with 1.6 million visitors over the six months it was open.

Here, some younger members of the Giles family making use of an opportunity. According to the newspaper report, the Museum was having difficulty in cataloguing a vast number of items and was considering seeking volunteer helpers.

'Hold tight, Grandma, here comes the Curse of Tutankhamun … POW!'

A change for the better?

'OK, Miss Mile End Rd. East – Like the poet Byron said " 'tis but a worthless world to win or lose."
Now git in 'ere and start cleaning it up.'

The morning after the night before.

'Beg pardon, Miss Fonteyn – this bit is not in Mr Como's script.'

The Royal Opera House was surrounded by the colourful life of the Covent Garden fruit, flowers and vegetables market until 1974, when the market moved out of the city centre, mainly due to traffic congestion.

'Wake up, Sleeping Beauty. We have information for thee.'

An interface between two distinct groups.

'Hop it, Apollo.'

Grandma and other members of the Giles family can be spotted in the crowd.

'Mitzi, can we have just one teeny-weeny smile like we're topless in St. Tropez?'

The Ship and Boat Builders National Federation (SBBNF) became the British Marine Federation seven years after this carton appeared.
Giles, an avid yachtsman, would have known all about adverse temperatures experienced on water in January, even when inside a building.

'We'd have looked handy nipping around in this lot on D Day.'

This cartoon shows Giles's skill in capturing the details of military uniforms with five different types illustrated..

'We appreciate you're new here, but should Her Majesty look in again, please don't ask her if her ticket is "legit" or did she get it on the market.'

The press reported problems with ticket touts. The young man was presumably only doing what he had been told to do.

The Military

The Military

Horse Guards Parade is a large parade ground just off Whitehall created in 1745 and formerly the site of the old Palace of Whitehall's tiltyard, where tournaments were held in the time of Henry VIII. It has been used for a variety of reviews, parades and other ceremonies since the seventeenth century. Above all, it is the site of the annual ceremonies of Trooping the Colour, which commemorates the monarch's official birthday. A number of military monuments and trophies ring the outside of the parade ground. The main building fronting the ground is Horse Guards – a large building in the Palladian style, built between 1751–53 to a design by William Kent. It is built on the site of the old Whitehall Palace. The building was the headquarters of the British Army's general staff and served as the offices of the commander-in-chief of the British Army until the post was abolished in 1904. It subsequently became the headquarters of the two major army commands – the London District and the Household Cavalry.

The Foot Guards' Regiments, of which the British Army has five, can be identified by, amongst other things, the spacing of the buttons on their tunics and the colour of their plumes as follows: Grenadier Guards, single-spaced buttons and white bearskin plumes; Coldstream Guards, buttons in pairs with red plumes; Scots Guards, buttons in threes and no plumes; Irish Guards, buttons in fours with blue plumes; Welsh Guards, buttons in fives and white/green/white plumes. The button spacing also indicates the order in which they were formed. When all five regiments parade together, the Grenadier Guards are on the right flank, then the Scots, Welsh and Irish Guards, with the Coldstream Guards on the left flank. Although the Coldstream Guards are ranked second in seniority, they form one of the flanks on the parade ground because their motto is 'Second to None'.

The Royal Hospital Chelsea is a retirement and nursing home for British soldiers who are unfit for further duty due to injury or old age. There are currently just over three hundred former soldiers, usually referred to as Chelsea Pensioners, resident at the Hospital. King Charles II founded the Hospital in 1682 in order to make provision for old or injured soldiers. Sir Christopher Wren was commissioned to design and erect the building and his design was based on the Hôpital des Invalides in Paris. Work on the Hospital was completed in February 1692 and by the end of the following month the full capacity of 476 former soldiers was in residence.

Parades. There are a number of major parades in central London each year, including the Lord Mayor's Show and the Notting Hill Carnival. The major parades involving military personnel are the annual Remembrance Day Parade at the Cenotaph in Whitehall and the Monarch's State Opening of Parliament Parade. Other major parades involving the military occur when there is a royal wedding or funeral, a funeral of an important person, such as Churchill, a visit by an important foreign monarch or dignitary, or the coronation of a new monarch. The annual State Opening of Parliament parade has changed little over the past five hundred years; it is performed at the start of the new Parliamentary year, usually in October or November or soon after an election. Several horse-drawn carriages are used to take the sovereign and ceremonial items from Buckingham Palace to the Palace of Westminster. The monarch is escorted by a large number of soldiers with a military band up front signalling to the crowds that the procession is about to arrive. The Household Division, as well as other members of the armed forces and the police, protects the route along which the procession passes. A quaint ritual is that a member of the government is held at the Palace as a 'hostage' during the ceremony and is released upon the monarch's safe return – a reminder of the days when there was a power struggle taking place between the monarchy and parliament.

'Apart from the 209,000,000 Russians watching the Trooping on TV, I shall be watching – so this year we'll try it without half of you falling feet over head.'

The Scots Guards' R.S.M. may have used a slightly more colourful phrase in reality. The BBC had arranged with the Moscow TV Central Network for the ceremony to be broadcast live to the Russians on 10 June. The BBC had, earlier in the year, broadcast live to the UK the May Day Parade in Moscow. The Queen's stand-in is taking his role very seriously.

'You should get a splendid view of Trooping the Colour from there madam – you're on the exact spot where Her Majesty will be taking the salute.'

The three buttons again identify the Scots Guards.

'What do you mean – I look like something out of Carnaby Street? I AM out of Carnaby Street.'

The two buttons, seen clearly on the Carnaby Street outfit, indicate the Coldstream Guards

'Here comes a male chauvinist pig if ever I saw one.'

Four buttons means that these are the Irish Guards.

"I'm off duty in ten minutes, when I shall show Davy Crockett here who's King of the Wild Frontier."

The four buttons grouping again tells us that these soldiers are Irish Guardsmen. The location may be a composite drawing based on Windsor Castle and St. James's Palace.

'Bertie couldn't stick his sergeant at Mafeking and he can't stick him leading the Armistice Parade today.'

Assuming that these old soldiers were twenty at the time of the Siege of Mafeking during the Boer War, they are ninety years old in the cartoon.

'Why the hell *shouldn't* I back Spurs to beat Chelsea if I want to!'

This is two days before the F.A. Cup Final at Wembley when, for the first time in the history of the competition, it was an all-London final with Tottenham Hotspur playing Chelsea. Spurs beat Chelsea 2–1. (See Battersea Power Station in the background.)

'You tell him he'll have to wait.'

*Coldstream Guards, probably on the Mall (location of Westminster Abbey adjusted to fit into the scene) for the Royal Wedding of Princess Margaret and Anthony Armstrong-Jones.
The crowds were so thick that the Commons had to be adjourned early, for the first time anyone could remember, because the Hansard reporters could not get through to the printers.
The West End was crammed solid with cars and people camping out.*

'There's a nasty story that a bit of a punch-up is going on between the officers and grooms of the Royal Mews.
Hey ho – off we go with the State Carriage to pick up today's royal visitors.'

This refers to the three-day state visit to London by King Baudouin and Queen Fabiola of Belgium. The newspapers reported that the Londoners 'turned out in their thousands
and gave them a very warm welcome'. The day before, a less warm relationship was reported involving a scuffle between several of the Queen's men,
resulting in an officer having a black eye and a groom being disciplined.

'Certainly they're mine. Finest team of Welsh sheep dogs that ever came to London, mun.'

Welsh sheep dogs rounding up Irish Guardsmen, on Horse Guards Parade.

'Reckon he heard you say if they did away with a few Horse Guards they'd have saved that extra 2d. on your fags.'

Visit by General and Mme de Gaulle. At a state banquet, he thanked Britain for taking on the burden of the war 'at a time when its own destiny, that of France and that of Europe hung upon it alone'.
Three days earlier the budget – announced in the press as 'A little-change Budget: dearer smoking' – had put two pence on the tax for a packet of twenty cigarettes.

'In view of the American general's observations on the British Forces, we will omit the first two bars of "Colonel Bogey".'

*A senior US military officer had stated the day before that he doubted the US had the 'stomach' to face up to the Soviet Union
and added that Britain's armed forces were 'pathetic' and were mostly generals, admirals and bands.*

Business and the Law

Business and the Law

The Royal Exchange was a centre for commerce in the City (it is now a shopping centre) and was originally established in 1565 by Sir Thomas Gresham in an attempt to supplant the bourse in Antwerp as the chief European market place. London merchants met here daily and it soon became the centre of the country's industry. Queen Elizabeth I formally opened the Exchange in 1571 and named it 'Royal'. The Exchange has been destroyed twice by fire and rebuilt on the same site on both occasions. The final Royal Exchange building was built in 1842 and was opened by Queen Victoria in October 1844 although trading did not begin in the building until the following January. The design has a stately Corinthian portico with a row of eight fluted columns surmounted by a large sculptured pediment. During the seventeenth century, stockbrokers were not allowed to use the Royal Exchange due to their 'rude manners', so they had to operate from other places in the vicinity, Jonathan's Coffee House in Change Lane being the most popular.

The London Stock Exchange is one of the world's oldest Stock Exchanges, with a three hundred-year history. It started life in the coffee houses of seventeenth- century-London when, in 1698, John Costaing began to issue 'at this office in Jonathan's Coffee House', a list of stock and commodities prices called 'The course of the Exchange and other things'. In 1972, Queen Elizabeth II opened the Exchange's new 26-storey office building and in 1973 the first female trading members were admitted to the market. In 2004, the Exchange moved from Frogmorton Street to its new headquarters in Paternoster Square, close to St. Paul's Cathedral. The London Stock Exchange is the most important exchange in Europe and one of the largest in the world. It lists over 3,000 companies with around 350 coming from fifty different countries and is considered to be the most international of all exchanges.

Inner Temple is one of the four Inns of Court around the Royal Courts of Justice, the others being Middle Temple, Gray's Inn, and Lincoln's Inn. The Inns of Court are the professional associations to one of which every English barrister must belong. The Temple area was occupied in the twelfth century by the Knights Templar, who built the Temple Church, which dates from the mid-twelfth century. The Inner Temple was first recorded as being used for legal purposes when lawyers' residences were burnt down during Wat Tyler's revolt in the 1380s.

The Royal Courts of Justice, known as Her Majesty's High Court of Justice, are situated on the Strand and comprise the Court of Appeal and the High Courts of Justice for England and Wales. The Courts were built in the 1870s to a Victorian Gothic design by George Edmund Street, a solicitor-turned-architect. Queen Victoria opened the building in 1882.

The Central Criminal Court, commonly known as the Old Bailey, is a Crown Court dealing with major criminal cases. E W Mountford designed the building in the Edwardian Baroque style, and it was completed in 1907. At the top of the dome on this building is the statue of Justice – a woman, holding in her right hand a sword standing for the power to punish, and in her left hand a balance standing for equity.

'There goes poor Percy – hijacked for the Exchange–Wall Street auxiliary cable service.'

*Another example where Giles has created a composite street scene. The left-hand side shows the Royal Exchange building, with the right hand side being 180 degrees in the opposite direction.
The cartoon refers to the overseas telephonists' strike – which started on January 20 and involved 2,000 London-based workers, then brought in all 3,500 telephonists in Britain, followed,
on 23 January by the 30,000 London postmen and sorters, and finally followed by the country's 185,000 postal workers – regarding banning overtime.
Agreement was reached on 1 February with the overseas telephonists getting the five per cent, they originally requested, backdated to August 1968 and a further two per cent to commence on 1 April.*

'Why are we sending you to negotiate with 'em? Because your missus is one of the ringleaders, that's why.'

The Members of the Exchange have left the former Birch's restaurant, (where, it was said, you could get the best sausages in London),
in Frogmorton Street opposite the then Stock Exchange, to dispel a phalanx of women intruders.
The day before, a move to allow women to become members of the Exchange was defeated 1,366 to 663 (all men, of course).
Women members were not allowed for another five years, though today the Exchange's chief executive is a female.

' 'Ullo, 'ullo, 'ullo!'

Inner Temple Lane seen from Fleet Street, with part of the Temple Church (featured in The Da Vinci Code) just in view at the bottom of the lane.
The idea of judges fighting in the street obviously appealed to Giles – Lord Chief Justice Lord Widgery had,
the previous day, ordered a retrial resulting in a verbal battle in court with the original judge involved.

'If you're going to agree with Mr Callaghan that it's legal to break the law, thou and I will be swelling the ranks of the unemployed.'

The TUC had set itself on a collision course with the Government by stating its intention to defy new laws curbing Union power with, if necessary, members going to prison rather than pay punitive fines. Former prime minister, Jim Callaghan, faced criticism for backing the TUC's call for action in support of the health workers.

'Of course I know who Lester Piggott is – he's the best midfield player Tottenham ever had.'

*The previous week, a judge had heard a plea by England's World Cup star, Paul Gasgoigne, to ban the publication of a book entitled 'Gazza', and asked who
'Gazza' was. Gazza's counsel replied 'a very well-known footballer'. The judge asked 'Rugby or Association Football?'
He then ruminated about there being an operetta called 'La Gazza Ladra' by Rossini, and finally kicked out the request,
believing that Gazza was insufficiently famous to warrant such treatment.*

'For allowing your car to be left 3 minutes beyond the allotted time on a yellow line twice in one year there is no punishment too severe. It is therefore my duty...!

A courtroom at the Central Criminal Court (also called the Old Bailey) with the figure of Justice atop the building's dome, seen through the window.
By this time, ten years after their introduction on the streets of London, traffic wardens had become one of Giles's pet hates.

Religion, Education and the Media

Religion, Education and the Media

Westminster Abbey (its official name is the Collegiate Church of St Peter, Westminster) is a mainly Gothic building. It is the customary place for the coronations of English monarchs. According to tradition, a shrine was first founded on the site in 616AD. The first stone Abbey was built around 1045–50 by Edward the Confessor, who had selected the site for his burial. The Abbey became the coronation site of Norman kings, but none was buried there until Henry III rebuilt the Abbey as a suitably regal place for his own tomb – under the highest Gothic nave in England. The work continued between 1245–1517 but was largely finished during the reign of Richard II (1367–1400). Nicholas Hawksmoor built the Abbey's two western towers between 1722–45. Until the nineteenth century, Westminster was the country's third seat of learning after Oxford and Cambridge. It was here that the first third of the King James Bible Old Testament and the last half of the New Testament were translated. The New English Bible was also compiled here in the twentieth century.

St Paul's Cathedral is an Anglican cathedral in the City of London and is the seat of the Bishop of London. It is believed to be the fifth St Paul's on the site; the present building dates from the seventeenth century. The first Saxon St Paul's was built in 604AD. The fourth St Paul's was begun by the Normans and was consecrated in 1240 but, almost immediately, an enlargement programme commenced; this work was completed in 1314. By the sixteenth century, this building was decaying badly and various works were undertaken to improve it, including a new West Front in the 1630s, by the classical architect Sir Inigo Jones. However, this building was destroyed in the Great Fire of London in 1666. The task of replacing it, along with fifty other city churches, was assigned to Christopher Wren in 1668. The final scheme was approved in 1675 and work began that year. The Cathedral was completed in 1708 on Wren's 76th birthday and was built from Portland stone and is in a late Renaissance style. St Peter's Basilica in Rome inspired its dome. The Cathedral has a substantial crypt holding over two hundred memorials.

Eton College was founded in 1440 by King Henry VI as a charity school to provide free education to seventy students who would go on to King's College at Cambridge. It is one of the nine original English public schools as defined by the Public Schools Act, 1868. Henry VI intended that the College Chapel nave should be the longest in Europe. However, Edward IV deposed him in 1461 and construction was stopped, with the nave having only eight bays instead of the seventeen or eighteen originally intended.

Express Newspapers' Offices, Fleet Street. In 1931, the Express Newspaper Group moved to 133 Fleet Street and its distinctive black 'art deco' building appears in some of the cartoons included in this book. It was designed by Sir Owen Williams and was, for almost sixty years, Fleet Street's most striking landmark. It remains a classic of Thirties design and, at its opening, was described as 'Britain's most modern building for Britain's most modern newspaper'. The newspaper group, now owned by Richard Desmond, moved from the building in 1989 and then to its present location in Lower Thames Street in 2004.

Broadcasting House is the headquarters of the BBC and was opened in May 1932. G Val Myer and the BBC civil engineer M T Tudsbery designed the exterior of the building, and the architect Raymond McGrath undertook the interior design – in a flowing Art Deco style – with a team including Serge Chemayeff and Wells Coates. It was later said of their efforts that 'the design for the BBC gave the first real fillip to industrial design in England'. The building is currently undergoing renovations with a scheduled completion in 2009/10.

'Another reason we hope you won't be sitting here tomorrow – your embrocation is upsetting our tracker dogs.'

The main entrance to the Abbey – Grandma is awaiting the wedding of Prince Andrew, Duke of York and Sarah Ferguson.

Sir Christopher Wren's famous dome, viewed from outside the old Express Group offices in Fleet Street. Chi-Chi and An-An, two giant pandas, were very much in the news,
having just been introduced to each other at London Zoo. The cartoon refers to the return to work, after a dispute that started on 5 August, when six hundred
men of the union representing, amongst others, newspaper blockmakers – were dismissed for failing to call off their work to rule decision in support of a claim for a £25 a week basic wage.

Battles
are won on
the
Playing Fields
of
ETON

ETON AND HARROW BEATEN AT EXAMS

'Oh yeah, yeah, yeah?'

Luptons Tower and a version of the College Chapel, seen above a wall introduced by Giles so that he could neatly tag the building.
In fact, the actual view is blocked by a three-storey college building – artistic licence again. A report by the Advisory Centre of Education, in researching A-level results, stated the statistical revelation that,
if there is any academic advantage to be gained by choice of school, it is in favour of the direct-grant and grammar schools against the independent public schools

'There's always one – she says she's taken the paper for 50 years and she wants her money back.'

Several members of the Giles family can be spotted enjoying the party, although one is her normal cantankerous self.

'When you've finished basking in all this reflected glory – one of you boys can slip out and get the Editor's tea!'

Maybe Giles saw himself, in his earlier years, as one of the young men enjoying the glory – possibly the one on the right.

'All yours Harry – stick it on display and get inside quick.'

The BBC was to publish its proposals for the pattern of national radio to meet the requirements of the 1970s, in July 1969, and wished to involve the public in the exercise.

Shopping and Hotels

Shopping and Hotels

Soho is an area of London, busy both day and night and home to a large mix of shops and services, bars and restaurants. Originally a royal park, by the seventeenth century it had been mostly sold off and underwent rapid development. It attracted many refugees in the eighteenth and nineteenth centuries. The mixture of nationalities gave the area a cosmopolitan reputation attracting writers, musicians, artists, and intellectuals. The end of the nineteenth century saw Soho establish itself as London's nightlife centre and late in the twentieth century it began to develop itself as a media centre, with a number of film companies settling there.

Carnaby Street was probably laid out in the late seventeenth century, but became known world-wide during the 1960s for its close association with the 'Swinging Sixties' period, when many independent shops, fashion boutiques and designers, were to be found there. Today, Carnaby Street is far more mainstream, being mostly chain stores and restaurants, with only a few independent shops.

Petticoat Lane is one of the oldest surviving markets in Britain. By 1608, it had become a commercial district where second-hand clothes and bric-a-brac were sold and exchanged and it became known as 'Peticote Lane'. In 1665, the aftermath of the Great Plague saw the rich flee from the east of London and property prices plummet. Then, in the late seventeenth century, a large number of Huguenots fleeing persecution settled in the area and many worked as master weavers. From the mid-eighteenth century, Petticoat Lane became a centre for manufacturing clothing and the market served the well-to-do in the City. Jews, fleeing from persecution in Eastern Europe, settled in the area from 1882, and many entered the local garment industry and maintained the traditions of the market. The area was badly bombed during the war and the Jewish communities dispersed; the market continued to prosper, though, with a new wave of immigrants from Asia in the 1970s. The lane was always renowned for the cockney patter and showmanship of the market traders. The market today remains busy and vibrant, reflecting both its multi-cultural history and its continuing popularity with locals and tourists.

London's Shopping Arcades are an attractive part of the city's shopping scene, usually accommodating up-market and boutique-type retail outlets. Perhaps the best known is Burlington Arcade, running between Piccadilly and Bond Street, and built in 1819. Other notable examples include Royal Arcade, between Albemarle Street and Old Bond Street; Royal Opera Arcade, the first in London; Piccadilly and Prince's Arcades, both off Piccadilly; and Leadenhall Market Arcade, off Bishopsgate.

The Savoy Hotel, opened in 1889, was built by Richard D'Oyly Carte, owner of the nearby Savoy Theatre. A feature of the hotel is that its forecourt is the only street in the United Kingdom where vehicles are required to drive on the right – it is said that this dates from the period when a cab drivers could open the passenger door on his side, which opened backwards with the handle at the front, without getting out of the vehicle while still allowing the passenger to alight directly onto the pavement . Claude Monet and James Whistler both stayed at the hotel and painted views of the Thames from their rooms.

Claridge's, a traditional grand hotel, has strong connections with royalty that have led it to be called an 'extension to Buckingham Palace'. Founded in 1812 as Mivarts Hotel, its reputation was confirmed in 1860 when Empress Eugenie, wife of Napoleon III, made an extended visit and entertained Queen Victoria there. Richard D'Oyly Carte purchased the old hotel in 1894, demolished it shortly afterwards and today's building opened in 1898.

'Pierre! Because Monsieur chooses to comment "Vive de Gaulle" you are not permitted to place the Consommé de Volaille on Monsieur's head.'

A typical corner in Soho. During a long period of unrest over Algeria, de Gaulle became Premier of France on 1 June 1958 and the National Assembly granted him emergency powers for six months.
The following days saw steel-helmeted riot squads firing warning shots over the heads of anti-de Gaulle demonstrators thronging the Champs Elysées and about one thousand de Gaullist supporters sweep down from the Arc de Triomphe.

'Pray tell us, Sire, shalt we repair unto yon café which we doth know as "Fred's", or to that fair tavern they calleth the Mucky Duck which art in King's Road, Chelsea?'

The prime minister Harold Wilson had stressed in the House of Commons the previous day that, if there was no agreement at inter-party talks on re-forming the House of Lords, the Government would go ahead with the necessary legislation. The cartoon dated three days later, included under 'the Houses of Parliament' section, also relates to this issue. Presumably some Peers have decided to cash in on the situation.

' 'Ullo 'ullo, what we got here?'

The previous day a woman had become Britain's first commercial surrogate mother. The deal was arranged through an agency and the childless married couple paid the woman and the agency £14,000 in total for the baby. The husband was the child's natural father through the process of artificial insemination.

'If we opened 365 days a week I expect Modom would still come bowling along at closing time for her reel of cotton?'

The Retail Distribution Association had just commenced discussions with the Shop, Distributive and Allied Workers Union about a five-day shopping week without all day closing on Saturdays.
It is difficult to know which of the arcades is portrayed. .

'One more two bob and we'll nip in for a soup and a roll.'

The day before, James Callaghan, the chancellor of the exchequer, had announced new taxes, but made it clear that he was anxious to avoid taxing necessities.
His tax changes, therefore, were designed to ensure that drinkers, drivers and smokers would all bear the burden.

'Thanks to Mr Kosygin's gift of vodka to our wonderful police bodyguard we've got to find him a new lot.'

Soviet Premier Alexey Kosygin was paying an eight-day official visit to London and the Soviet party stayed at Claridge's.
London's police chief broke a rule to allow some of his men to receive gifts of vodka and cigars from Mr Kosygin at the end of his stay.
The Russian security men paid a huge compliment to the Special Branch by saying, 'We can trust you and we are going shopping', which they did.

Sport

Sport

The **Henley Royal Regatta** is held on the river Thames. The first regatta was staged in 1839 and has been known as the Henley Royal Regatta since 1851, when Prince Albert became the first royal patron. Since his death, every reigning monarch has agreed to be its patron. During 1908 and 1948, when London hosted the Olympic Games, rowing races were held on the regatta course. The regatta lasts for five days, and the most prestigious event is the Grand Challenge Cup for Men's Eights, which has been awarded since the regatta's beginning.

The University Boat Race is held each spring on the Thames between the rowing clubs of Cambridge and Oxford Universities. With 2004's television audience of more than half a billion viewers, it makes the race one of the most watched sports in the world. The first race was held in 1829 and it has been held annually since 1856 with the exception of the years comprising the two world wars. The course is 6,779 metres (four miles, 374 yards) and the race is for heavyweight eights (eight rowers with a Cox steering, and no restrictions on weight). The tradition started with Charles Merivale, a student at Cambridge with a school friend studying at Oxford, Charles Wordsworth. Cambridge challenged Oxford to a race and the challenge was repeated the following year. Score-to-date: Cambridge – 79 wins, Oxford – 73 wins, 1 dead heat (In 1877, the race was declared a dead heat – on a course of over four miles!).

Wimbledon – the Championships at Wimbledon are the oldest and arguably the most prestigious event in the sport of tennis. The Championships were first played under the control of the All England Lawn Tennis and Croquet Club in 1877 at a ground near Worple Road in Wimbledon – the only event being the Gentlemen's Singles. In 1884, the Ladies' Singles and Gentlemen's Doubles were added, and Ladies' Doubles and Mixed Doubles added in 1913. The Championship moved to its present site in 1922. There are 19 courts, the major courts being Centre Court and No.1 Court and are normally only used for the Championships and tickets for these two courts are always in high demand. The remaining seventeen courts are regularly used for other events throughout the year hosted by the All England Lawn Tennis and Croquet Club.

Wembley – the English national football stadium. First known as the Empire Stadium, the original stadium was built for the British Empire Exhibition of 1924. Sir John Simpson and Maxwell Ayrton were the architects and its two distinctive Twin Towers, now demolished as part of the recent rebuilding scheme, became its trademark. Its official maximum capacity was 127,000 but it is believed that this was greatly exceeded on a number of occasions. It was the venue for the first Olympic Games after World War II. In 1948. Pele, the famous Brazilian footballer, said, "Wembley is the church of football. It is the capital of football and the heart of football," in recognition of the world's best-known football stadium.

Royal Ascot – used for thoroughbred horse racing and closely associated with the Royal Family, it is one of the leading racecourses in the United Kingdom. Queen Anne founded it in 1711, and the first race, 'Her Majesty's Plate' with a purse of one hundred guineas, was held in August of that year. In 1813, Parliament passed an Act to ensure that the grounds would remain a public racecourse. Until 1945, the only racing that took place was the Royal Meeting, a four-day event. Since then, more fixtures have been introduced, notably the steeplechase and hurdles in 1965. Royal Ascot is one of the world's most famous race meetings with members of the Royal Family arriving each day in a horse-drawn carriage.

Epsom is the racecourse on the North Downs. It is best known for hosting the Epsom Derby, the United Kingdom's premier flat, thoroughbred horse race for three-year-old fillies and colts and covers one-and-a-half miles. The Twelfth Earl of Derby instituted the Derby in 1780.

'I expect it's those Tory dockers sabotaging the Communists this time, don't you, Daddy?'

This is one way of looking at it. An unofficial seaman's strike resulted in a call at government level for a 'new look' in industrial relations.

'Ain't that nice, Butch? You'll be able to tell the folks back home you nearly saw the Boat Race.'

This is more a comment on British weather than on the race.

'There goes my 7 to 4 bet – according to that tic-tac man one of the players has belted a linesman before the game's started.'

The Romanian player Ilie Nastase had been disqualified the previous month at Bournemouth for arguing with the British umpire, and the previous year by an American umpire at the championships in Indianapolis, for using bad language. Both umpires were on duty at Wimbledon and there was some speculation about what would happen. In the event, the only incident was when Nastase kissed the hand of a lady line judge who had called one of his shots 'out', only to be over-ruled by the umpire.

'Ladies! Let's keep our Women's Lib. activities off the Centre Court.'

A period of bitterness in the women's tennis world with the 'Women's Lib' group strongly pursuing their cause.
At the same time 'Kool Pants', created by the British designer Teddy Tinling, were the hottest thing at that year's Wimbledon with most female players sporting them.

'What was that for? For dancing your —— horses all over our —— pitch, that's what that was for.'

The stadium – with its famous two towers – has now been demolished and replaced by the new stadium, with its highly distinctive arch.
This cartoon portrays another of the clashes between groups within our society.

'You say "Your Majesty" if you bump into the Queen. Not Jean Rook.'

*The Royal Enclosure on Ladies Day where everyone must wear a hat – even the horse is sporting a topper. Note the man who has taken the rule literally.
Jean Rook, fellow journalist, was more than once the subject of Giles's humour and, on her first day with the paper, the front page had Giles Jnr. bawling
'Down with Women's Lib – sack Jean Rook before she starts'..*

'Ascot Illusion … Going the wrong way, anyway.'

Hermoine Gingold was a flamboyant actress, born in England, she died in the States. She attended Ascot for the first time in 1952 and wrote an article for the Express, which accompanied this cartoon, declaring that "Ascot is so very naice". Giles is portraying her here in a very elevated position. Is that Giles up there beside her?

Epsom

Grandma used that whip at a number of sporting events, including going to Wembley to cheer on her beloved Ipswich Town football team at the 1978 Cup Final, which they won.

Transport

Transport

London Buses are one of London's principal icons, the archetypal red rear entrance double-decker being recognised worldwide. Buses were first introduced to the streets of London in 1829 when George Shillibeer started operating his horse-drawn omnibus service from Paddington to the City. Horse-drawn carriages ran up to 1914. Until the 1960s, London went its own way regarding buses, designing its own vehicles especially for London use rather than using the bus manufacturer's standard products used elsewhere. The last bus specifically designed for London was the AEC Routemaster, which was introduced to the London streets in 1956. Since the turn of the Millennium, there has been a shift to low-floor, double-deck and articulated buses, though the Routemaster is still used on two heritage routes in central London.

London Cabs. The first hackney carriage licenses date from 1662 and applied literally to horse-drawn carriages for hire; they were later modernised to hansom cabs in 1834. Electric carriages appeared in 1897, but were not reliable; 1903 saw the introduction of the internal combustion engine vehicles for hire. The last horse-drawn hackney carriage ceased service in 1947. Today, the motorised cabs are traditionally black, although other colours can be seen.

London Underground is an all-electric railway system that covers much of the Greater London conurbation. It is the world's oldest underground system and is one of the largest in route length – 408 kilometres (253 miles). Service began in 1863 with the Metropolitan Railway between Paddington and Farringdon Street. In the years 2005–06, total passenger journeys reached a record level of 971 million, and since March, 2007, over three million have used it per day.

The River Thames is one of the major waterways in England and by the eighteenth century was one of the world's busiest waterways, with London at the centre of the vast mercantile British Empire. The advent of rail and improved road transportation, coupled with the decline of the Empire in the years following the end of the First World War, reduced the prominence of the river. A number of companies provide tourist cruises trips and ferry services along the main London stretch of the river.

Gridlock/Traffic. Like most major world cities, London suffers from severe traffic congestion. The city introduced congestion charging in 2003 for the central zone – the first large-scale congestion charge scheme to be introduced in the UK – and this has brought about significant improvements. The zone was extended in spring 2007 to incorporate the western areas of London.

Victoria Railway Station is one of the mainline railway stations serving London. The railway line to this station has its origins in the Great Exhibition of 1851, though the early station wasn't built until 1862; it was rebuilt in the early twentieth century.

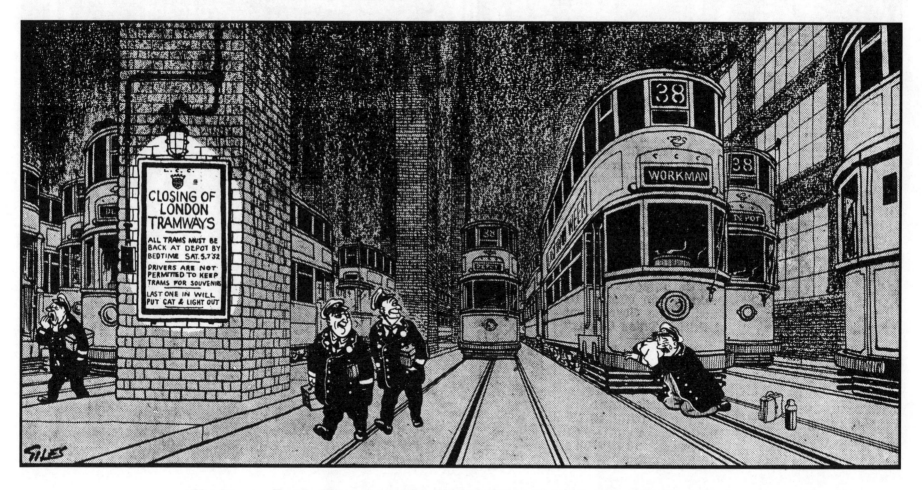

'If you saw Fred's Missus you'd understand him being in love with his tram.'

Class E/1 trams, built in batches between 1907–29, remained in service until the closure of London's tramways system in 1952.
Route 38 went along the Embankment via Westminster and the Workman was a special service.

'Don't you "hurry-for'ard-landlubber" me, you sea serpent.'

This is a typical double-deck, rear-entrance London bus. It is fairly certain that a number of Giles's sailing friends are illustrated in the queue.
Giles could be the one in the chequered jacket, with seaweed stuck to his bare feet.
Also shown is an example of the 'friendly' type of London conductor.

**'Compliments of the Shah of Persia, lady – he's sorry he's got a date at Buckingham Palace, SW1,
the same time as you've got one with your sister Millie in Kensington, SW7.'**

An example of the earlier cabs with the open side, alongside the driver, to take luggage. Note the Routemaster bus behind the cab.

You see all sorts of people on the tube.

'These yours? We found them stowed away in the Trans-Antarctic expedition ship.'

The ship, the 'Magga Dan', was taking the Commonwealth Trans-Antarctic Expedition, which left Butler's Wharf that day, on a 9,000-mile voyage to the Shackleton Base in the Antarctic. Was Grandma intending to go to the Antarctic as an adventure, or did she really mean to go somewhere warmer than this country at this time of the year and jump ship part way?

'He's got a point – there isn't one that says "No Fatstock".'

Was Giles, a keen car driver, making a point about the ever-increasing number of traffic signs in London?

'There's a lot of mumbling afoot that if we don't get a move on it will defeat the purpose of the trip.'

The Hyde Park Corner Screen, near Piccadilly, forms the backcloth to this cartoon. Aspley House, shown on the right, was the London home of the Duke of Wellington and now houses the Wellington Museum.
A director of one of Denmark's abortion clinics had just announced that they could cut the cost of British abortions by up to fifty per cent and added
'since last week we have had a steady stream (from Britain) of girls and housewives from sixteen to forty-five years of age'.

'It won't be Mr Kosygin who'll take the can back because Grandma waited at the wrong airport.'

Due to fog, Mr Kosygin's plane had to divert from Gatwick to Heathrow. Grandma was not the only one caught out: the plane had to circle around
London for a while to give the prime minister Harold Wilson time to get from Gatwick to Heathrow to welcome the visitor.
Odd that an ardent supporter of royalty like Grandma should wish to give the Soviet Premier such a warm welcome …
or is it? Remember, it is Grandma.

London Characters

London Characters

Giles's London cartoons are peopled with an amazing range of characters reflecting what is regularly seen on the streets of the city. In some cases, the fashions may have changed, but the essential range of people from all backgrounds is still there. You will see uniformed policemen and women, bus drivers (not so many conductors nowadays), traffic wardens (who come in for a lot of stick from Giles's more wicked side), servicemen and women (usually the former) of all ranks as well as a wide array of office workers, shoppers, manual workers, and foreign and other visitors to the city.

A particular feature of many of Giles's London cartoons is the humour created by a 'collision' of people from completely different walks of life: the uptight ceremonial type having to converse with the cheeky cockney; the 'seen-it-all-before' London policemen having to deal with a group of rustic gentlemen in town for the Agricultural Show or a group of weekend sailors in London for the Boat Show; or the genteel spectators mixing with a more carefree spirit over strawberries and cream at Wimbledon. This conflict is frequently at the core of Giles's humour, and is an essential part of his cartoon world.

'If they tread on Grandma's toes many more times, it'll bang goodbye to the "no violence either side" pact.'

*The wonderful British bobby – each policeman's face tells a story. The occasion was a demonstration by the Committee of One Hundred against nuclear arms policies.
It was a passive battle waged between thousands of demonstrators sitting down on the road and refusing to move, and a strong force of police.
Almost nine hundred people were arrested in Trafalgar Square in the two-and-a-half-hour 'battle'.*

'Nice start, Henry.'

The following day, traffic wardens were introduced on the streets of central London for the first time, where they issued 344 tickets.
Motorists gave them a mixed reception: there were some comments about over-zealousness and one man contacted the AA to say
'he had been given a ticket for stopping in the wrong place for only five minutes'.

'All aboard for the Spring Fashion Show – strawberry and cream checks, white daisy patterns, lovely pastel colours.'

The humorous variety of the London bus conductor – to be compared favourably with the other sort illustrated in the earlier cartoon relating to London buses.

'My advert didn't say anything about luxury. It said six-berth accommodation for the Jubilee, stone's throw from the Palace, Continental visitors welcome.'

Tourists flooded into London for Elizabeth II's silver jubilee. There was great concern about sufficient accommodation for tourists and, the previous day, the London Tourist Board had felt it necessary to announce that 'accommodation was still available and the situation was not as grave as painted'. Note Battersea Power Station in the background.

'If there's a thing I dislike more than a Labour MP who filibusts me all night it's a Labour MP who thinks he's going to keep me another hour discussing his home team's chances in the Cup.'

Members of Parliament meet the city's early morning life. Note the time is 5.05am, from the days when Parliament did all-night sittings.
On 16 February, the Commons sitting started at 2.30pm and did not finish until breakfast the next day.
It was the result of a form of 'political warfare' in which the Opposition kept asking questions (sixty-seven in total) designed to hold up business.

'D'you know what Oi'd do to solve Lunnun's traffic problem, young Gentleman?
Oi'd plough the damn lot up – that's what Oi'd do.'

Country boys meet city gents. After a period of great concern about Britain's increasing traffic congestion problems, particularly in London, the government had announced, the previous week, a considerable increase in expenditure on new and improved roads rising from the then present £5m a year to between £14m and £15m a year by 1957/8.

"Off home, all of you, before I charge you with being dressed in a manner likely to cause a breach of the peace.'

The Law meets the sailing fraternity. The Daily Express article at the time suggested that people should 'step out of the winter into the salty breezes of summer at Olympia'.

'I suppose if the master tailors' strike had affected Savile Row, we should automatically have become a race of intellectuals.'

The moneyed class meets the thinkers. The reference is to the threatened closure of their premises by the Master Ladies' Tailors Organisation regarding workers' pay.
It employed between 15,000 and 20,000 men, and wished to guarantee an £8 per week wage with the possibility of workers earning a bonus to take their pay up to £16.
The Tailors and Garments Worker's Union rejected the idea, believing that it would result in an overall loss of pay.

'Fifty to one against selling these cowboys tickets for Liberace OR Bolshoi.'

The shires meet the city boys.

'He's got very nice manners – every time he steals a strawberry he says "Thanks, doll".'

The fading middle-class meets a young radical at Wimbledon. Following the great success of the earlier Band Aid for Africa concert,
many of the Wimbledon stars decided to give five per cent of any cash prizes to a Tennis Players Aid for Africa campaign.
Possibly, the young man felt that he could benefit from the general sense of generosity to be found at this year's Championships.

'Dad handed his war medals in protest against the Poll Tax, but the Corporal told him to take them home and clean 'em up.'

The 'man-in-the-street' meets the might of the British Army, at the corner pier outside Buckingham Palace.

'It's not Black Rod, m'Lord – the lady has left her box of Persil just behind the Throne.'

Bigwigs from the corridors of power meet their match at the entrance to the House of Lords. The Director General of the BBC told a meeting with businessmen in Cardiff that the Corporation was totally opposed to advertising on television as a means of raising money, as its programme standards would undoubtedly drop.